Boffin Boy and the Worm of Death
by David Orme

Illustrated by Peter Richardson

Published by Ransom Publishing Ltd.
Radley House, 8 St Cross Road, Winchester, Hants. SO23 9HX
www.ransom.co.uk

ISBN   978 178127 051 6
First published in 2013
Reprinted 2014
Copyright © 2013 Ransom Publishing Ltd.

Illustrations copyright © 2013 Peter Richardson

A CIP catalogue record of this book is available from the British Library.

Design & layout: *redpaperdesign.co.uk*
Find out more about Boffin Boy at *www.ransom.co.uk*.

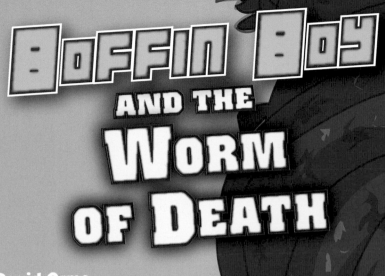

Boffin Boy
AND THE
Worm
of Death

By David Orme
Illustrated by Peter Richardson

Ransom

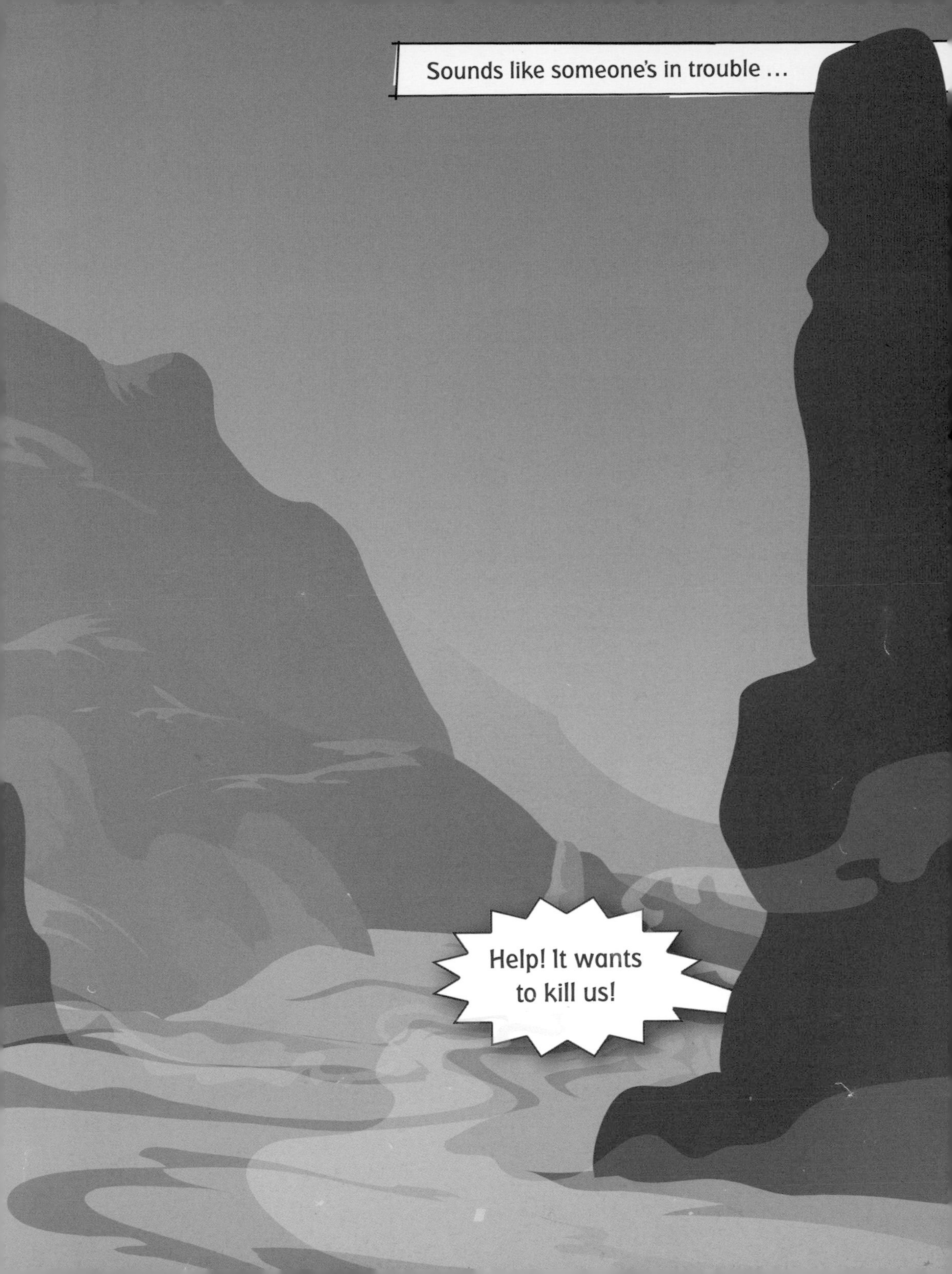
Sounds like someone's in trouble ...
Help! It wants to kill us!

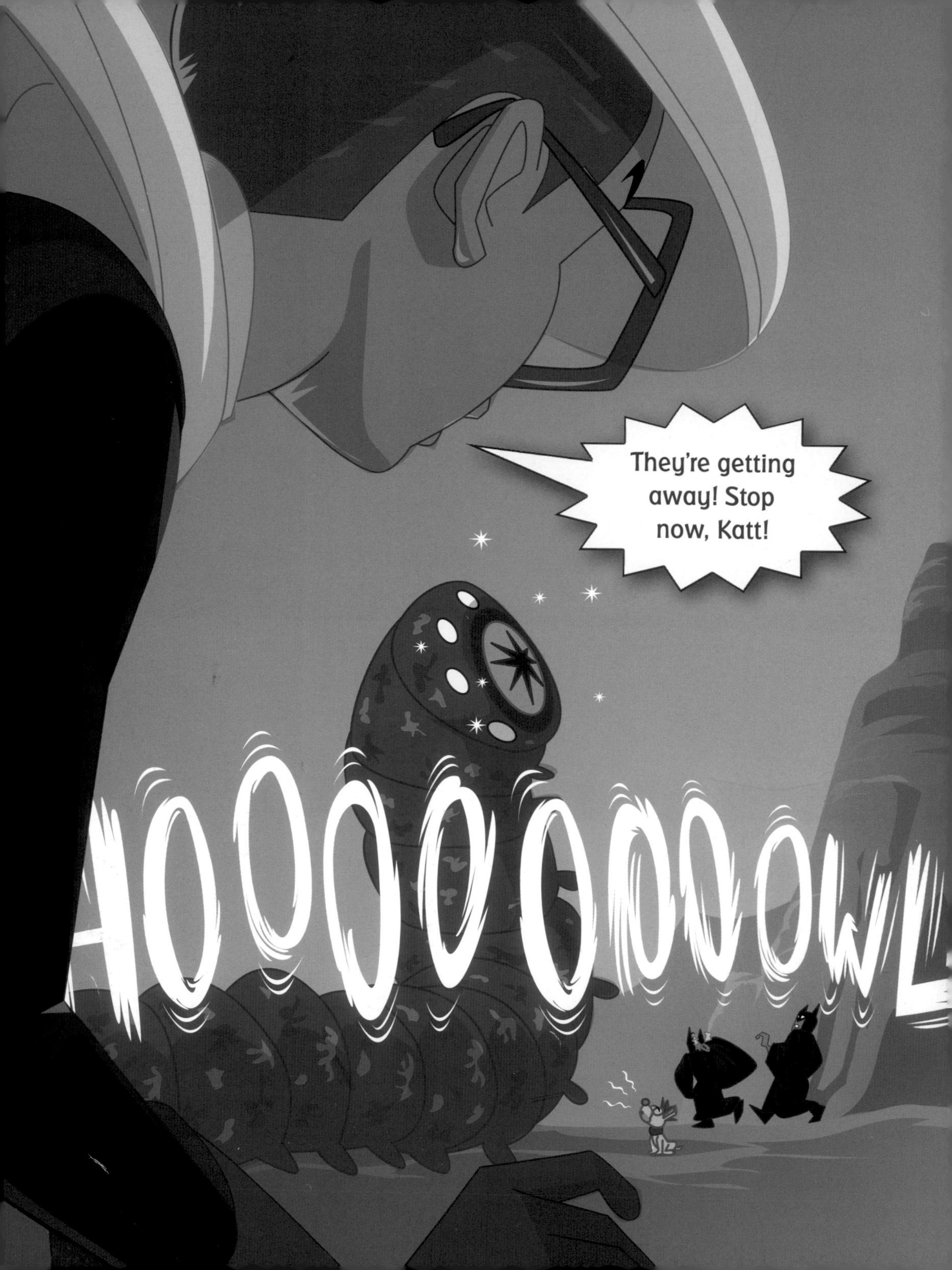
They're getting away! Stop now, Katt!
HOOOOOOOOWL